SCHOLASTIC

Leveled

Readers

Ten Racing Rats

By Jack Booth • Illustrated by Christopher Jones

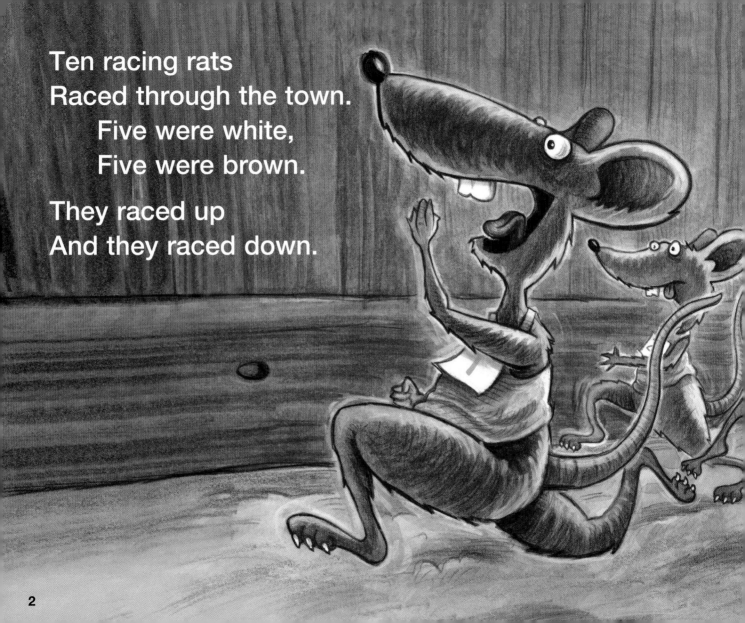

Ten racing rats
Raced through the town.
　　Five were white,
　　Five were brown.

They raced up
And they raced down.

2

Ten racing rats
Raced through the town.

Ten prancing ponies
Pranced through the town.
Six were white,
Four were brown.

They pranced up
And they pranced down.

Ten prancing ponies
Pranced through the town.

Ten leaping lizards
Leaped through the town.
    Seven were white,
    Three were brown.

They leaped up
And they leaped down.

Ten leaping lizards
Leaped through the town.

Ten galloping giraffes
Galloped through the town.
Eight were white,
Two were brown.

They galloped up
And they galloped down.

Ten galloping giraffes
Galloped through the town.

9

Ten waddling walruses
Waddled through the town.
   Nine were white,
   One was brown.

They waddled up
And they waddled down.

Ten waddling walruses
Waddled through the town.

Ten bouncing bunnies
Bounced through the town.
　　Ten were white,
　　None were brown.

They bounced up
And they bounced down.

Ten bouncing bunnies
Bounced out of the town.

Notes for Teachers and Families

- Read the poem with the children. Invite them to demonstrate each verb — racing, prancing, leaping, gliding, waddling, bouncing.

- Model the poem using two different colored linking cubes, counters, or stickers. Invite children to create the different combinations in the book to make 10 (e.g., 5 white cubes and 5 brown cubes to show the brown and white rats adding up to 10).

- On a chart, write the corresponding addition story for each illustration.
  E.g., $5 + 5 = 10$ $6 + 4 = 10$ $7 + 3 = 10$

- Invite the children to explore other ways of combining two numbers together to make 10.

- Trim an egg carton so there are places for 10 eggs. Provide the children with counters or cubes of different colors. Invite children to fill up the carton (one in each egg holder). Children can count the number of each color they used. You may wish to record the different combinations on chart paper using algorithms or images.

- Arrange 10 counters in a row with some of them covered by an index card or an upside down cup, etc. Ask children to determine how many counters are covered out of the 10 and how many are left. Invite children to explain how they arrived at their answer.

- Children can create a new illustration for this story. They can choose an animal from this book or another one that they might wish to draw. Children can use two different colors for their animals. They can determine how many of each color they wish to draw.

  Note: Some children might write a new verse to accompany the illustration using the pattern of this book.